Tips for Reading Together

Children learn best when reading is fun.

- Talk about the title and the pictures on the cover.
- Discuss what you think the story might be about.
- Read the story together, inviting your child to read with you.
- Give lots of praise as your child reads with you, and help them when necessary.
- Try different ways of helping if they get stuck on a word. For example: read the first sound or syllable of the word, read the whole sentence, or refer to the picture. Focus on the meaning.
- Have fun finding the hidden nuts.
- Re-read the story later, encouraging your child to read as much of it as they can.

Children enjoy re-reading stories and this helps to build their confidence.

Have fun!

Find the 10 nuts hidden in the pictures.
There are 2 of each of these.

Missing!

Roderick Hunt • Alex Brychta

OXFORD
UNIVERSITY PRESS

Nadim had a hamster.

He called it Jaws.

"Jaws is a funny name for
a hamster," said Biff.

Nadim put Jaws in his cage, but
he forgot to shut the cage door.

Jaws got out of the cage and
ran away.

Nadim saw the cage was open.

"Oh no!" he said.

Nadim was upset.

"Jaws has run away," he said.

The children looked for Jaws.

They looked and looked.

Biff looked under the sink.

Chip looked in the fridge.

Nadim looked under the
cupboard.

Nadim's Dad looked for Jaws.

He pulled up the floorboards.

"Maybe Jaws is down here,"
he said.

Then Chip had an idea.

"Let's get Floppy," he said.

"He can find Jaws."

Sniff, sniff, went Floppy.

Sniff, sniff! SNIFF! SNIFF!

"Look in here," said Chip.

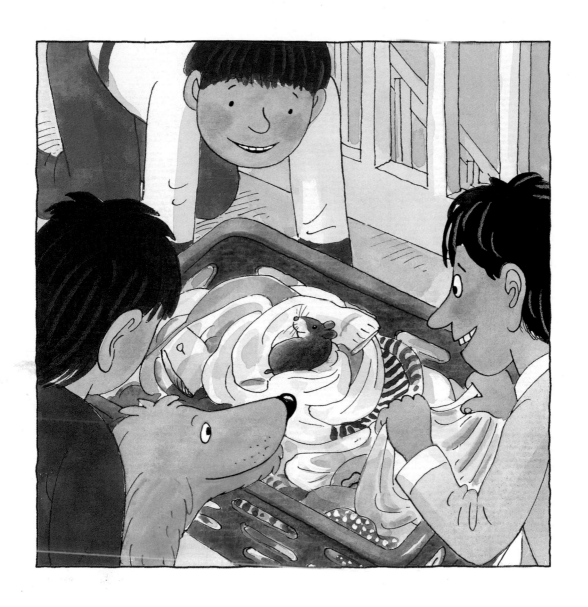

Jaws was in the clothes basket.

He had made a nest.

"Look!" said Nadim. "You can
see why I called him Jaws."

Think about the story

Why is the hamster called Jaws?

Why was Nadim upset when he found that Jaws had run away?

Where did the children and Dad look for Jaws?

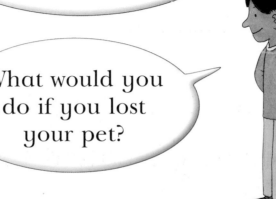

What would you do if you lost your pet?

Odd one out

Which two things don't begin with the same sound as the
'**h**' at the beginning of '**h**amster'?

More books for you to enjoy

Level 1:
Getting Ready

Level 2:
Starting to Read

Level 3:
Becoming a Reader

Level 4:
Building Confidence

Level 5:
Reading with
Confidence

OXFORD
UNIVERSITY PRESS

Great Clarendon Street,
Oxford OX2 6DP

Text © Roderick Hunt 2006
Illustrations © Alex Brychta 2006

First published 2006
All rights reserved

Series Editors: Kate Ruttle,
Annemarie Young

British Library Cataloguing
in Publication Data available

ISBN–13: 978-019-279231-0

10 9 8 7 6 5 4 3 2

Printed in China by Imago